SPACE WARP

FREEDOM IS LOST.

EVERYWHERE TYRANNY RULES,
EVERYWHERE SWELLING SORROW
AND THIS IS PLEASING TO US.

BEFORE THE WARP LORDS, THE ARMIES
OF ENDLESS EARTHS SHALL GROAN
LET US USE OUR WARP CROWNS
TO WREAK HAVOC UPON THEM!

THE INTOXICATION OF DRINKING
HUMAN PAIN CAUSES ME TO SPEAK
THE CHIEF OBJECT OF MY OBSERVATION IS
THE RETALIATOR, FROM THE POOL OF LYVER

IT WILL BE MY PART TO SPEAK
OF HER REPROACHFULLY FOR SHE,
TOO, BEARS A WARP CROWN

ANGELIC HER FACE, SHE YET BEARS
THE MARK OF THE DAMNED

HER HAND THREATENS THE
PORTALS BETWEEN THE EARTHS

I EARNESTLY LONG FOR HER BLOOD,
PLEASANT THAT THOUGHT

THE VISITATION OF THE GRAVE FOR HER
WITH A SLIGHT IMPULSE OF OUR WRATH!

FROM THE PROPHECIES OF THE WARP LORDS, THE NECRONOMICON OF MALEK

NOW MEET **THE HEROES** FIGHTING **THE TERRORS OF THE WARP!**

HIDE AND SURVIVE

It is too late for you to leave the City of Liverpool. The Emergency Services are not coming. You live in a Front Line City, and we cannot guarantee your safety. Seek shelter as the Dinosaurs approach. Find a safe place and wait for the danger to pass.

You have probably caught the virus carried by the Dinosaurs when they came through the Warp. There is a 95% chance you will not survive. If you do, this leaflet will give you some handy tips on how to deal with Dinosaur attacks.

STAY SILENT

You are now living in a city with no traffic or other city noise. Dinosaurs have acute hearing. Any noise could attract them. So move around as little as possible inside your Refuge. Place mattresses against the walls to reduce sound.
If you feel the need to scream, scream into a cushion. Outside, we recommend you wear a gag at all times.
Remember: Silence is Survival.

CONTROL YOUR FEAR

Good places to hide: cupboard under the stairs; in the bath with a mattress over you; under the bed; in a wardrobe. It is not safe to go outside. If you must leave your house and you meet a T Rex or other predator, do not excite it or provoke it in any way. Walk calmly and slowly backwards, then turn and run in a straight line. Running in a zig-zag pattern will only slow you down. If you are cornered, lie down and place a bag over your head.

SAVE THE SOUTH

The North and West of Britain have now succumbed to the Warp. Our priority must be to save the South. Do not try to leave. All roads to the South have been cut. The Security Forces have orders to take extreme measures against anyone trying to break through the safety cordon.

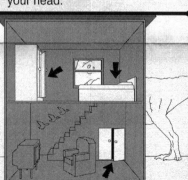

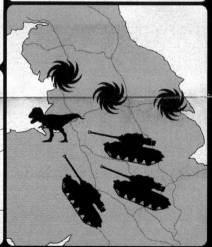

STAY SILENT   **CONTROL YOUR FEAR**   **SAVE THE SOUTH**

For more Useful Advice and a Survivor's Glossary go to Spacewarpcomic.com

JURASSIC PUNX

MAYBE TONIGHT.

MAYBE.

MAYBE TONIGHT I'LL BE REUNITED WITH THEM.

MAYBE.

I'VE BEEN COMING HERE EVERY NIGHT FOR THE LAST TWO YEARS.

EVER SINCE *FAN DAY*.

WHEN THE WARP OPENED AND *THE INVADERS* CAME THROUGH.

AND *ANNIE, LUCY* AND *JAKE* WERE TRAPPED ON *THE FAR SIDE* IN BIRKENHEAD.

MAYBE TONIGHT IT WILL OPEN AGAIN AND I CAN FIND THEM.

MAYBE.

STORY: PAT MILLS
ART: BRUNO STAHL
LETTERING: MIKE D

HELLBREAKER PROLOGUE

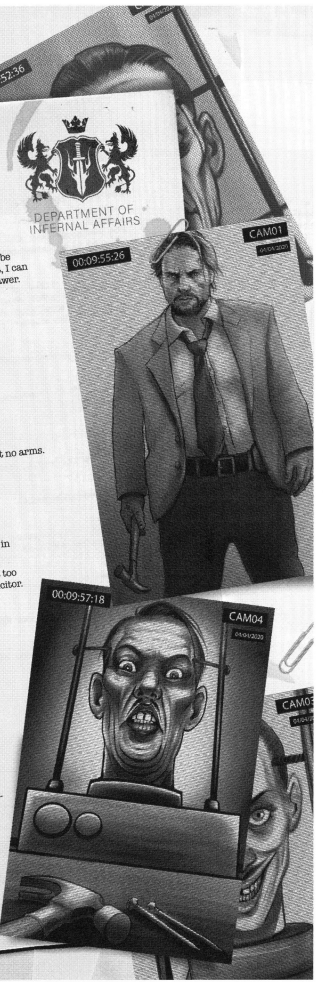

Covert Camera Operator's Log 1128.
Target - Asquith, Rod - Detective Sergeant - D.I.A.
Allegations - Use of Excessive Force on an Infernal, Perverting the Course of Justice.
Report: George McDonald.
Interview Room Number Two - D.I.A. Headquarters.
Time/Date Stamp. (0950, APRIL 4 2020)
Present - DS Asquith D.I.A.
Richter - Escaped Dead Person - Head only.

DS Asquith - This interview is not being videotaped or audio recorded. What would be the point? You're an undead scumbag with zero rights. A Hellbreaker. If I feel like it, I can blow you apart or keep you in a shoebox next to a bottle of Scotch in my bottom drawer.

Richter – Scotch? You strike me more as a Baileys kinda guy.

- DC Asquith produces a hammer and nails and lays them out in front of Richter.

Richter - Planning on doing some DIY, copper?

DS Asquith - I plan on hammering nails through your eyeballs until I get the answers I want. You're a lawyer who escaped from Hell, right?

Richter - I bet you do a lot of DIY at home. Bet Mrs Pig likes to keep you busy.

DC Asquith threatens to drive a nail into Richter's forehead.

DS Asquith - I've never nailed a brief before.

Richter - Noooo!

DS Asquith - Or how about your nose? Got an urge to scratch it? But you've got no arms.

Richter - So funny, you must be a real laugh at the Masons!

DS Asquith - I'm serious.

Richter – Alright, Sarge! Let me breathe a second will ya?

DS Asquith -That's kind of difficult. You ain't got any lungs either.

Richter - All right! All right! Well, I'm sure you've guessed by now that being in Circle 6 of Hell isn't easy for someone with my natural good looks.

DS Asquith - Don't play me for a fool Richter. Circle 6 is for people who tweet too much, eat on the Tube and can't pronounce 'Falafel'. You were a Defence Solicitor. Don't get any lower than that, my chum. You're Circle 9.

Richter – (groans) Yeah, alright. I'm Circle 9.

DS Asquith - So, how'd you die?

Richter - Got strung up by an angry mob in Ipswich after, may I say, brilliantly defending a man wrongly accused of terrible crimes.

DS Asquith - Wrongly?

Richter - Well... so he said. I didn't really believe him but I found a loophole and got him off. I'm clever like that.

DS Asquith - Not that clever as those locals hung you for it.

Richter - Even my brilliant legal mind has its limits.

DS Asquith - And you went to Hell straightaway?

Richter – Sadly, yes. No real trial to speak of. Some Ultors appeared out of the void, grabbed me and carted me off kicking and screaming to Hell. Due Process didn't even occur to them! They kind of remind me of you!

DS Asquith - Thanks, very nice of you to say so.

Richter - Can you put the nails away now?

DS Asquith - Nope. But carry on please.

Richter - What else do you need to know? I was in Hell with no chance of parole and then I escaped!

DS Asquith - What about De La Rue? How'd you two meet?

Richter - Studying Cosmic Law in Hell. The Ultors like us to understand our crimes. Guilt boosts the punishment. Kept himself to himself, though. Brooding type.

DS Asquith - So if he kept himself to himself, how'd you two get so chummy?

Richter - I could tell just by looking at him he was planning something. He had that air about him. Didn't speak to anyone who might endanger his plan. Very shrewd.

DS Asquith - So you got alongside him?

Richter - Yeah. Showed I could be trusted, got under his skin so to speak.

DS Asquith - You seem good at that. Then?

Richter - Somehow he was tipped off the Warp was about to open the Gates of Hell.

DS Asquith - And you both escaped. What's De La Rue doing here now?

Richter - Oh, he'll be on another mission.

DS Asquith - Mission? What does that mean? Mission for who?

Richter - You guys up for a deal?

DC Asquith takes out his handgun.

DS Asquith - I can let you regenerate, then blow your head off again, if that would jog your memory?

Richter - Nah, a real deal, Sarge. I'll tell you everything and you don't send me back to Hell.

DS Asquith points his gun at Richter.

Richter - Listen, hurt me all you want but it's nothing compared to what the Ultors will do to me.

DS Asquith - I'll need a taste of what you got to go to The Bishop and the Judge with.

Richter - Oh, negotiation! Just my favourite thing!

DS Asquith - Who is Slayer?

Richter - You got me. Not a clue.

DS Asquith - Interesting... Cos, I've heard that this Slayer gave Rue a miniature Warp that allows him to create dimensional gates and disguise his appearance?

Richter - Maybe? Now let's talk about that deal.

DS Asquith - In a minute... Rue thinks he's some kind of Cosmic Law Enforcer now? That's why he's got three million followers on Instagram.. There are prats out there who believe he's some kind of freaking Robin Hood.

Richter - Deal!

DS Asquith - How about the girl? Tease me with something about her that I can go to their Lordships with.

Richter - You know about Stephanie? Yeah, she's a real piece of work.

DS Asquith - How'd she get ED?

Richter - How most of the chicks get sent to Eternal Damnation: selling drugs. She done it wholesale with containers full of the stuff.

DS Asquith - Strange. If Rue is so High an' Mighty then how'd the two of them hook up.

Richter - Love. Yeah, can you believe it? The idiot says he's in love! There is no love in Hell, don't ya know!

(Interruption to Interview - Detective Inspector McNeal enters room).

DS Asquith - Oh, crap!

Richter: A DI?! Oh, she's gonna kick your ass, Asquith!

Detective Inspector McNeal - DS Asquith, would you kindly remove the nails?

DS Asquith - Yes, guv.

Detective Inspector McNeal - And return the hammer to the evidence store. It's required in court tomorrow.

DS Asquith - Yes, guv.

Detective Inspector McNeal - Now please leave.

DS Asquith - (sighs) Yes, guv.

Richter - Hahahahahahahahahahahahahahah!

(1020 - Interview Suspended)

De La Rue

Stephanie

(1055 - Interview Commences)

Present in Interview Room with Richter -
Detective Inspector McNeal, The Archbishop, His Grace Justin Campbell and Judge Charles Rayner.

Detective Inspector McNeal - Now, Richter, let's start again shall we? Tell me how you and De La Rue escaped from Hell.

DIS, CAPITAL CITY OF HELL. THE NINTH CIRCLE.

STORY
PAT MILLS
ART
IAN ASHCROFT
LETTERING
MIKE DONALDSON

HELLBREAKER

ATTENTION! ATTENTION! THIS IS A LOCKDOWN! THREE PRISONERS TRYING TO ESCAPE! ALL INMATES RETURN TO THEIR CELLS! OR FACE FOURTH DEGREE **CRUCIATION!**

AND THIS *WARP'S* DEFINITELY THERE?

OTHER SIDE OF THE *GATES!* TRUST ME!

BUT *NO ONE'S* EVER ESCAPED BEFORE!

WARPSTAR ACADEMY
NOTICE BOARD

BE WORTHY — BE MANLY — BE BELLIGERENT

ONE EARTH IS NOT ENOUGH

THE SCHOOL ANTHEM

THE FUTURE OF THE PLANET'S AT STAKE
ENTER THE HEROES NO ALIEN CAN BREAK
FU-TANTS! PROTECTING THE EARTH!
FU-TANTS! THE WARP GAVE BIRTH!
FOR EVERY THREAT, A HERO TRUE!
ALPHA TO OMEGA, A FUTANT FOR YOU!
INVENTORS, PSYCHICS, SOLDIERS OF RENOWN,
EVERY FUTURE MUTANT DESERVES A CROWN.
POWERS OF INVISIBILITY, POWERS OF THE BRAIN,
POWERS OF STRENGTH, POWERS OVER PAIN.
WATCH! GUARD! DEFEND! NIGHT AND DAY!
LORD PROTECTOR DROGEDA SHOWS US THE WAY!

School Trip

I'm looking forward – with a group of my Alpha pupils – to visiting the mysterious 12th century **Church of the Apocalypse** in the Vall de Boi, Northern Spain.
It is the only Church to show paintings of the Apocalypse and no one knows why! Perhaps my brightest pupils will finally decode its secrets? My own theory? The paintings are actually depictions of the terrifying realities on Alternate Earths that were caused by the cosmic event known as Spatium Torquent!
The Space Warp!

More images from the Church can be seen on our school website.

A MESSAGE FROM YOUR HEADMASTER FU TOBIAS DROGEDA MA Oxon

The end of term is nearly upon us as you **Future Mutants** undergo the Final Submersions that will confirm your **Warp powers**. It reminds me of how I achieved my own incredible powers. As a 17th century Alchemist, I searched for many years for the **Secret of Eternal Life**. Finally, I discovered it at the **Battle of Drogheda** where my master Oliver Cromwell deemed it necessary to put all 3,500 defenders of the town to the sword. The barbarous Irish wretches had refused to surrender, you see. But their deaths were not in vain. I was able to draw on their **soul energy** so I could live forever. So a part of them lives on through me. Isn't that incredible? It's why I adapted my name from the town.

EDEN CANDIDATES

We are pleased to announce the lucky pupils listed on page two have been selected for **Eden**. Congratulations! Don't be disappointed that you didn't make the grade as Future Mutants. Instead, an exciting, new and different Future awaits you on Eden! Please pack your personal belongings and be ready for space embarkation at **0700 hours tomorrow**.

For more important messages from Headmaster Drogeda visit
Spacewarpcomic.com/fu-tant

PAT MILLS   MIKE DONALDSON
FU☀TANT

WHEN I LOOK OUT AT THE STARS, I AM REMINDED OF *THE INFINITE EARTHS* CREATED BY *THE WARP*. SO NEAR AND YET SO FAR, IN NEED OF OUR PROTECTION.

I YEARN TO BE *LORD PROTECTOR* OF THOSE WORLDS BECAUSE... *ONE EARTH IS NOT ENOUGH.*

AND WITH YOUR HELP I SHALL SUCCEED. IT'S WHY *YOU* WERE CHOSEN FOR *WARPSTAR ACADEMY.*

DIE, DAMN YOU! DIE!

THE *WARP LORDS* HAVE SENT IN THE *HOSTILES.*

BECAUSE THEY KNOW DROGEDA'S DREAM IS TO BE *LORD PROTECTOR OF INFINITE EARTHS.*

YOU'D THINK *OVER 400 YEARS* HE WOULD HAVE *MATURED.*

AND REALISED THERE'S A LOT MORE TO LIFE.

BUT *NO.* HE'S *STILL* ALL ABOUT *POWER, FEAR* AND *WINNING.*

KODA! LISTEN TO ME!

APOCALYPSE HOW?

IT'S HOW HIS PROTECTORATE WORKS. YOU'RE *ONLY* PROMOTED IF HE'S GOT SOME *DIRT* ON YOU. OR FOUND *ANOTHER WAY* TO *BRIBE* OR *CONTROL* YOU.

IF I TAKE THE PAINTINGS BACK TO *THE WARPSTAR*, DROGEDA WILL HAVE *MURKAL* AND HIS TEAM OF *GENIUSES* FIGURE OUT THEIR MEANING. DISCOVER *WHERE* THE *PORTALS* ARE.

AND I KNOW WHAT HAPPENS IF I *DON'T*...

MY FRIENDS DIE.

THEY'RE PAINTINGS OF WHAT LOOK LIKE *DINOSAURS*... *GIANT MICROBES*... *ALIENS*... *KNIGHTS*... *DEMONS FROM HELL*... *LIFE ON OTHER EARTHS*.

WHOEVER THE *FU-TANT* WAS WHO PAINTED THEM AND *WHY*, I DON'T KNOW YET.

BUT *THE FUTURE* OF THOSE OTHER EARTHS COULD DEPEND UPON ME *FINDING OUT*.

APOCALYPSE HOW?

RETURN TO THE WARPSTAR IN *SPACEWARP* PHASE TWO!

 **SPECIAL FORCES ONE**
Elite combat unit
formed by Stellar Union
of Humans, Aliens and
Robots to help liberate
the planet Crater from
the Alien Junkarrs.

Both the Union and the Junkarrs want Crater for its
valuable shoals of Makrobes; giant microbes that swarm
in the skies and craters of the planet.

The war between the Union and the Junkarrs - known as the
QUANTUM WAR - has been going on for hundreds of years.

THE VIRAKS

Bacteria Eating Viruses
weaponized by the Junkarrs
to attack Union forces.
The Viraks inject their
DNA into their prey, where
it reproduces and then
explodes out of the host.

THE MISSION   ## SF1 ROLL CALL   ## THE ENEMY

BAD DOG
< Human >
Maori heritage.
Recommended for SF1 after
being diagnosed with
PTSE: Post traumatic
stress enjoyment.
Hates all Makrobes,
especially the Viraks.

KRAK SHOT
< Robot >
Enjoys robots' superior
status to Humans, following
the Galactic Council's
ruling that Humans are 57%
Bacteria and are therefore
a legitimate target
for the Viraks.

MORLOK
< Alien >
Able to tune the microbes in his
own body with the Viraks and is
thus safe from their attacks.
'They're nature's cleaners.Dustmen.
They dispose of bacteria. If
nothing got eaten, there'd be dead
bodies piled high as mountains.'

DEATHNAUT
< Robot >
Programmed to be a peacemaker.
He believes peace will
come if humans talk to the
'enemy within', and find a
way to make contact with
the viruses and bacteria
inside themselves.

SALOME
< Human >
Agrees with Deathnaut.
She hears her bacteria
'singing' inside her, but
can't make sense of their
songs. She tries to silence
them with alcohol.

HOMICIDA
< Alien >
Her race lay their eggs
on Crater and need the
Makrobes to help them
feed their young. After
mating, the males are given
the great honour of being
killed by the females.

RULING BY THE GALACTIC HIGH COUNCIL

In 2568, the Council rejected the Humans' last appeal for recognition. The GHC Chief Judge
gave this ruling: 'You Humans are made up of 57% bacteria and therefore they, not you, are
the majority. Whereas your enemy, the Junkarrs, are only 25% bacteria and they control their
micro-organisms. But you Humans are ruled entirely by your emotions with catastrophic results.
These feelings come from your gut, your 'second brain', where your bacteria and viruses are most
plentiful. Tests have proved it's your micro-organisms who are really making your decisions,
not you. You are nothing more than their puppets. Your human rights are accordingly revoked.'

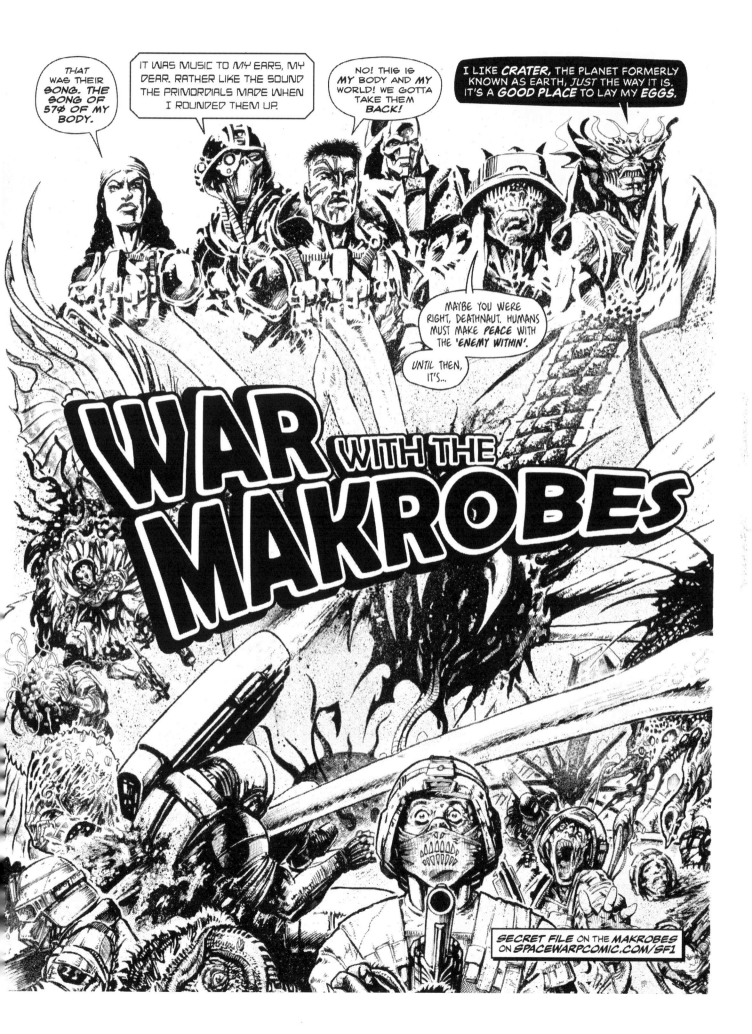

SLAYER

STORY
PAT MILLS
ART
JAMES NEWELL

"If civilisation were to be found
on other planets and
if it were feasible to communicate,
then we would want to
send missionaries to save them,
just as we did in the past when
new lands were discovered."

Father Chris Corbally, Vatican Observatory,
Mount Graham, Arizona.
Deputy director of the Jesuit project
searching for Alien life.
Sunday Times 14th December 1999

THE MISSIONARY SHIP *CONQUISTADOR*, ABOVE THE
PLANET COLUMBUS (FORMERLY CALLED *NAJAKA*).

MY FELLOW
CRUSADERS, NOW
IT'S THE NAJAKS'
TURN TO BE
SAVED!

ALL HAIL
*THE
WARPED
ROSE!*

THE 'HEROES' AWAKEN THE HUMAN CATTLE
THEIR ACTS DETER PRAISEWORTHY PILLAGE
JOYLESS THIS MAKES ME
VIOLENT EXERTIONS ARE REQUIRED
IN A WRATHFUL MANNER
IN A BUTCHERING MANNER
COFFINS FOR THEM ALL!

FROM THE PROPHECIES OF THE WARP LORDS, THE NECRONOMICON OF MALEK

END OF PHASE ONE

SPACEWARP CREW

PUBLISHER: Millsverse Comics EDITORS: Lisa & Pat Mills ART EDITOR: Vince Hunt QUANTUM MECHANIC: Schlock aka Slayer
FRESH START PROGRAM: Doctor Zot MD. Sole distributor Tachyon Hypershields™. Reiki Master (Level 3)

FRONT AND BACK COVER
Drawing: Mike Donaldson Colours: Gareth Sleightholme

WRITER CREATOR
Pat Mills

ARTIST CREATORS
DOC ZOT: Charles Gillespie FU-TANT: Mike Donaldson HELLBREAKER: Ian Ashcroft JURASSIC PUNX: Bruno Stahl SF1: Ade Hughes
SFEER & LOATHING (Warp Lords): Gareth Sleightholme SLAYER: James Newell XECUTIONERS: Gareth Sleightholme
FUTURE SCHLOCK 'BRANDED!' (Free story with newsletter sign-up): Cliff Cumber

LETTERERS
Mike Donaldson: Fu-Tant, Hellbreaker, Jurassic Punx
James Newell: Slayer, Sfeer & Loathing
Ken Reynolds: SF1, Xecutioners, Future Schlock Branded!, Doc Zot

FEATURE PAGES
HELLBREAKER PROLOGUE STORY: George McDonald ART: Ian Ashcroft DESIGN: Vince Hunt

FEATURE PAGES TEXT: Lisa & Pat Mills

ALL FEATURE PAGES DESIGNED BY: Vince Hunt
Except where listed below:

PAGE 1 WARP SPIRAL PAINTING: Simon Hodgkiss-Rogers PAGES 1 & 68 DESIGN: The Prophecies of the Warp Lords: Phil Vaughan PAG
& 3 ADVERT DESIGN: Vince Hunt and Lisa Mills 'FOLLOW ME'! ART: Darren Cullen
HIDE & SURVIVE ART & DESIGN: Mike Donaldson FU-TANT NOTICEBOARD ART & DESIGN: Mike Donaldson
MERCH & SPACEWARP CREW PAGE: Unpaid intern

SPACEWARP MASTHEAD DESIGN Margarita Mustafina, Lisa Mills, Vince Hunt

WEB DEVELOPER Caro Begin WEB TRAILER Phil Vaughan

SPECIAL THANKS TO: Caro Begin, Simon Hodgkiss-Rogers, George McDonald, Phil Vaughan. And to all Spacewarp Creators.

EXTRA SPECIAL THANKS TO OUR BETA READERS: Gwyn Ap Harri & pupils of XP school; Daniel Borge & friends; Ian Ashcroft;
Stephen Brotherstone for a Liverpool look at Jurassic Punx; Sarah Harris; Chris & Theo Mitchell; John Ottaway;
Derek, Alicia & Paris at The San Pedro Bookshop.

COPYRIGHT

IN THE EVENT THAT THE WARP LORDS CAUSE A WAVE FUNCTION COLLAPSE: AVOID GENE POOLS. DO NOT ADJUST YOUR REALITY. RIDE THE WAVE!

The Quantum Mechanic's Galactic Handbook